Scholastic Inc.
New York Toronto London Auckland Sydney Mexico City New Delhi Hong Kong Buenos Aires

Kids Are Authors®
Books written by children for children

The Kids Are Authors® Competition was established in 1986 to encourage children to read and to become involved in the creative process of writing.

Since then, thousands of children have written and illustrated books as participants in the Kids Are Authors® Competition.

The winning books in the annual competition are published by Scholastic Inc. and are distributed by Scholastic Book Fairs throughout the United States.

For more information:
Kids Are Authors® 1080 Greenwood Blvd.; Lake Mary, FL 32746
Or visit our web site at: www.scholastic.com/kidsareauthors

ISBN-10: 0-545-04881-8

ISBN-13: 978-0-545-04881-1

12 11 10 9 8 7 6 5 4 3 2 1

Cover and Book Design by Bill Henderson

Printed and bound in the U.S.A.
First Printing, June 2007

POOR PLUTO!

While we were working on our solar system dioramas, our teacher made a very shocking announcement.

"Class, scientists have just decided that Pluto can no longer be a planet. Now, there are only 8 planets, so please remove him from your project. I'm sorry."

We cried, "POOR PLUTO!"

Pluto didn't have a family anymore!
How sad! How terrible!
We knew we had to do something!

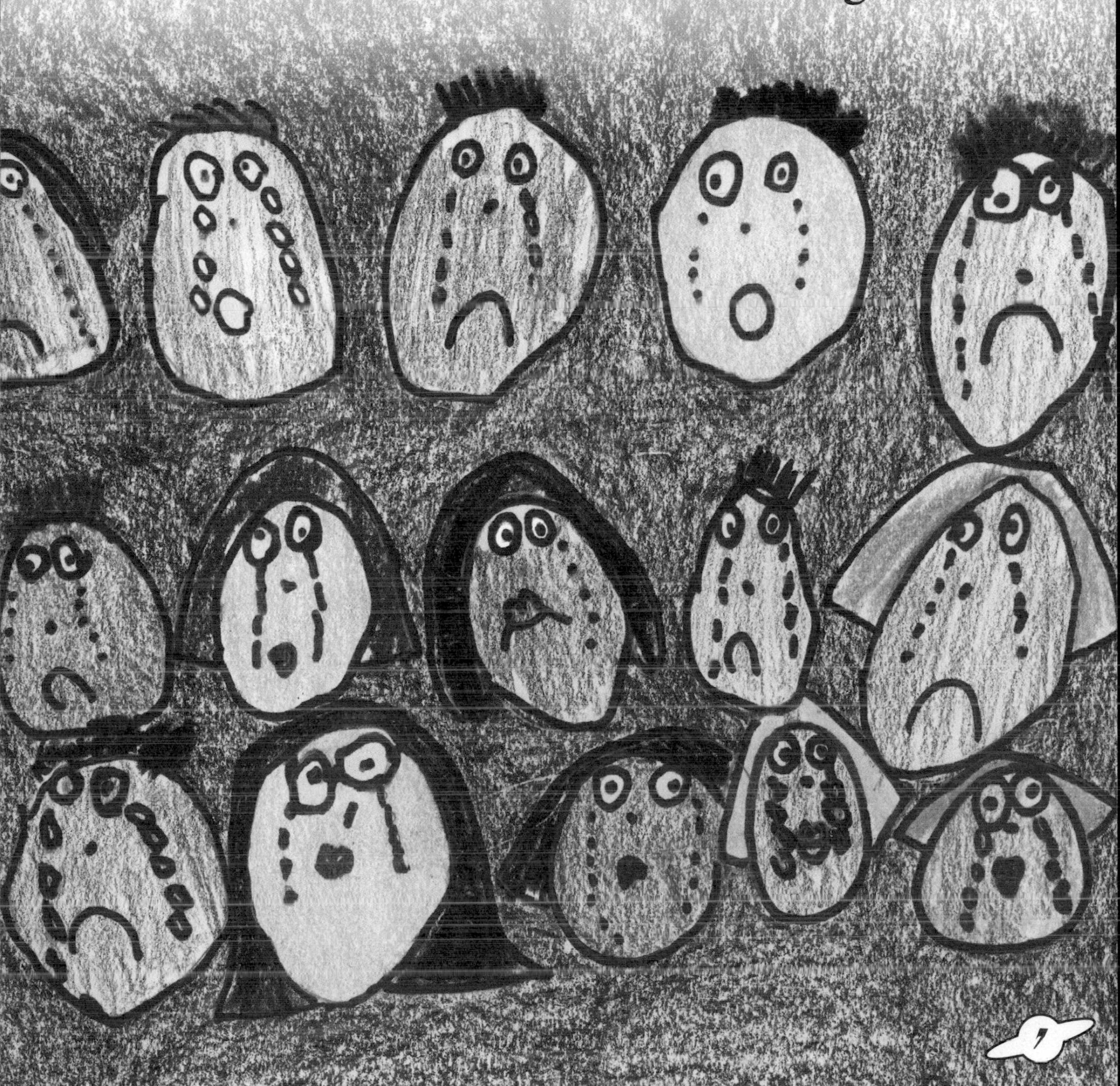

So during recess, we collected materials from around our school and built a rocket ship.

It was big enough to hold 16 students, 1 teacher, and 3 pet hamsters.

We asked our principal if we could go. He didn't mind. So, we blasted off to find Pluto.

10...

9...

8...

7...

6...

5...

4...

3...

2...

1...

BLAST OFF!

HURRY BACK!

It was great being in outer space. Our mission was to find Pluto and bring him back with us so he wouldn't feel lonely. We would be his new family!

After we passed all of the planets,

we saw Pluto!

We got a huge rope, tied a lasso, tossed it around Pluto, and brought him into our rocket.

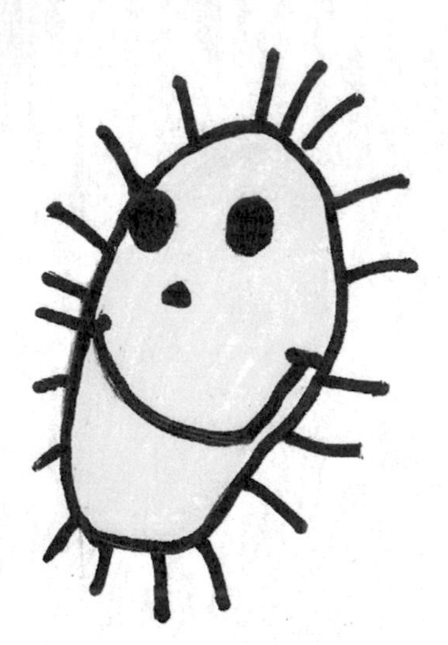

When we returned to our school, we had so much fun with Pluto.

We rolled down the slide together...

…and played tetherball.

But when we took our timed tests, Pluto couldn't hold a pencil.

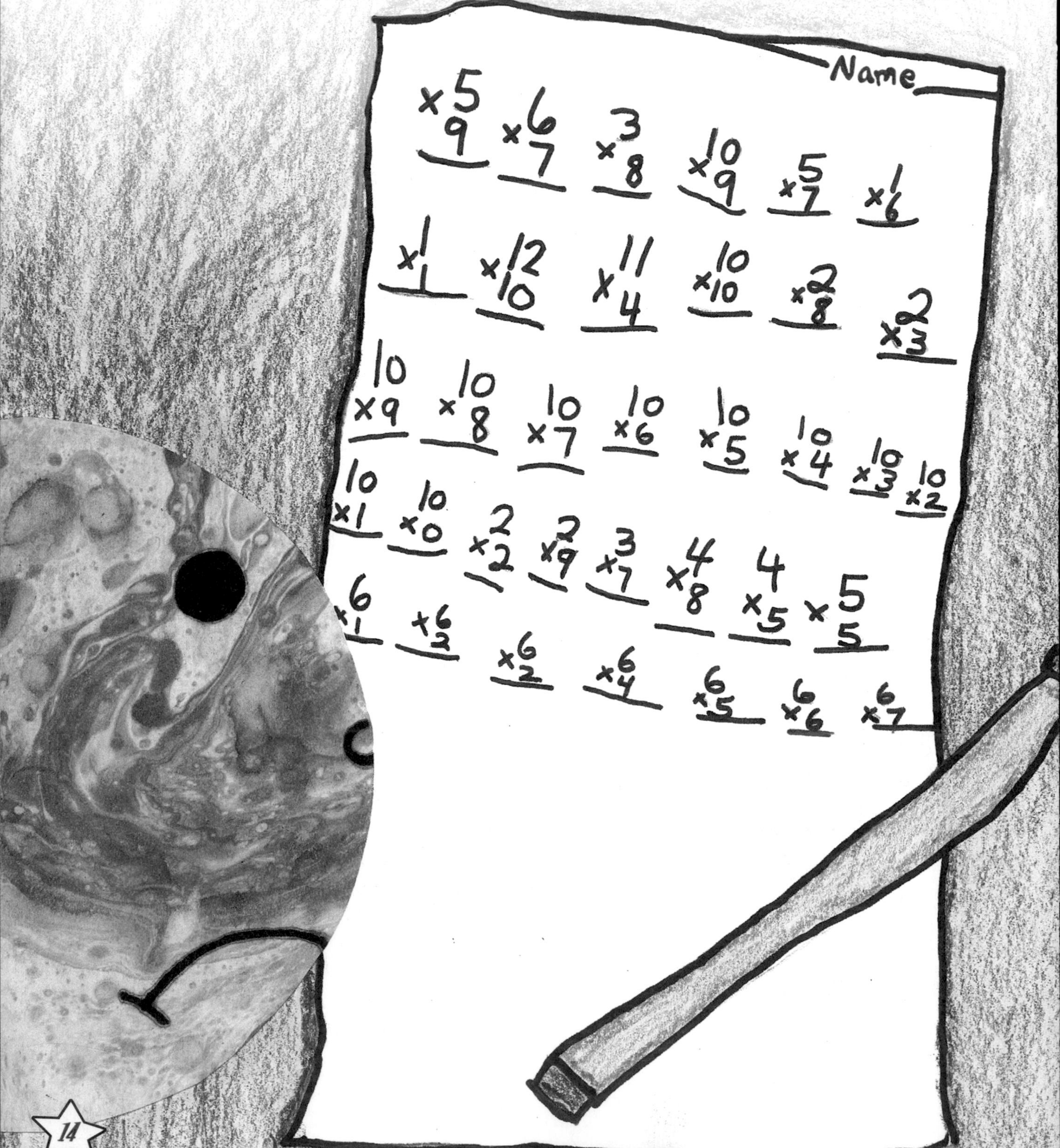

And when Pluto tried to sit,

the desk broke.

The saddest part of the day was when Becky, the bus driver, shouted,

"NO PLANETS ON THE BUS!"

So, we all went home. Pluto stayed alone in our classroom overnight. As darkness came, he looked out the window and way up into the sky.

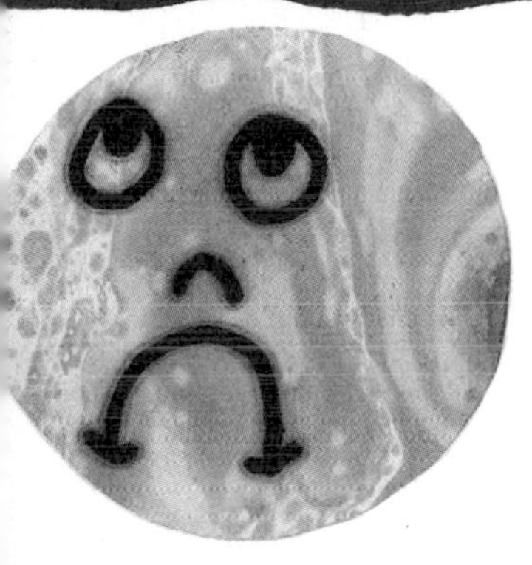

He could see his old friends way off in the distance. Carol Comet, Mike Meteor, Stanley Star, and Billy Blackhole.

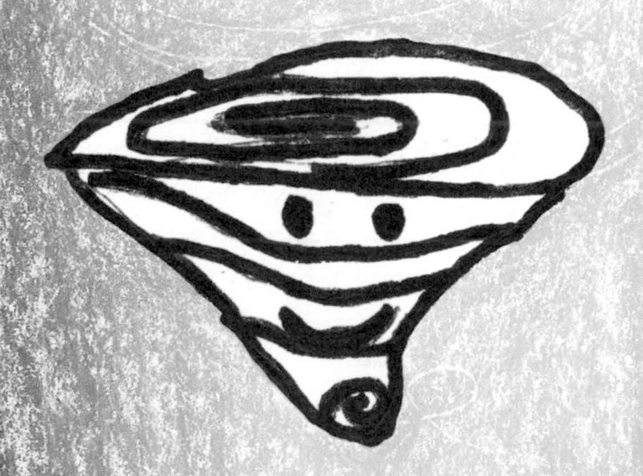

He missed them very much.

He cried big planet tears.

After we saw how sad Pluto was in our classroom, we knew he had to go back home. Even though he wasn't a real planet anymore, he still belonged to the solar system family.

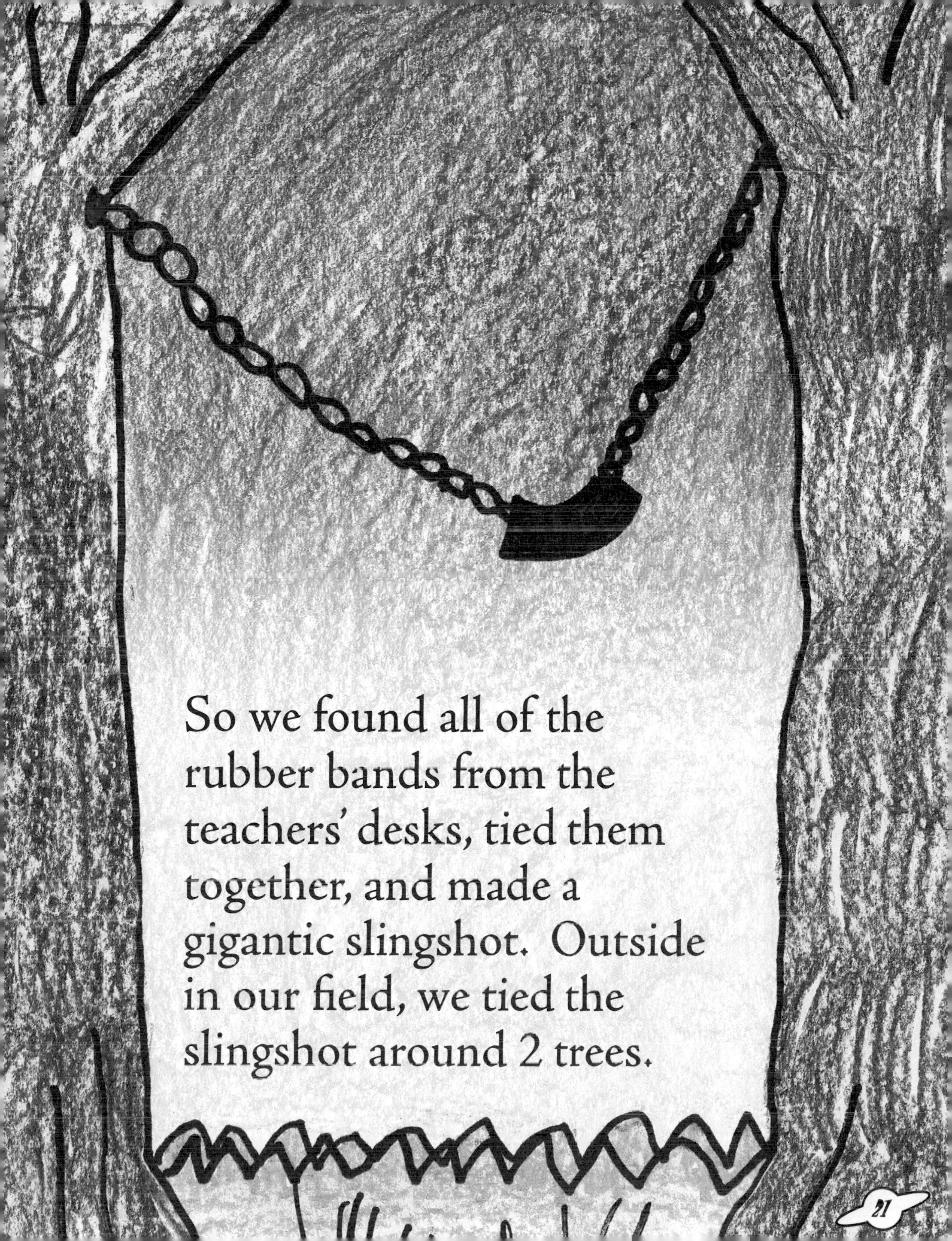

So we found all of the rubber bands from the teachers' desks, tied them together, and made a gigantic slingshot. Outside in our field, we tied the slingshot around 2 trees.

Pluto said goodbye to us.
We said goodbye to Pluto.

"GOODBYE!"

We tucked Pluto safely inside the slingshot and pulled it back as far as it would go. And then,

BLAST OFF!

Pluto blasted across the sky, all the way back to his place in the solar system. Right where he belongs!

We will never forget the
year we tried to save Pluto.
Guess what?
He didn't need saving.
He was just fine!

THE END

How to Make a Solar System Diorama

- Find an empty box and paint it black.
- Spatter white paint to look like stars.
- Lay the box on its side and poke 8 holes on the top. Use a nail.
- Cut 8 planet shapes out of cardboard and paint them.

- Poke holes in the planets and tie strings through the holes.

- Make a large cardboard sun and glue it to the end of the box.
- Add stars, comets, asteroids, and anything else from the solar system (and don't forget **PLUTO!**).

What Really Happened to Pluto?

On Thursday, August 17, 2006, the International Astronomical Union decided that Pluto was no longer going to be classified as a planet. They say in order for an object to be called a planet, it must orbit around a star, have a round shape, and have enough gravity to have its own orbit path. Pluto does orbit a star, but it has a more oval shape and doesn't have its own orbit path. (It shares an orbit path with Neptune.) So, now there are only 8 real planets and Pluto is something else. It may be called a Dwarf Planet or a Pluton.

Nobody is quite sure yet.

MEET THE AUTHORS

Top row from left to right: Nikki Karapanos, Penny Irwin, Alondra Ponce, Erin Ott, Jorge Toscano, David Charco
Middle row: Brennon Berninger, Carlos Flores, Anthony Juarez
Bottom row: Shelby Chipman, Jonathan Davis, Stephanie Gonzales, Brandi Din, Ramiro Rodriguez, Guadalupe Alonzo, Anthony Cadena
Project Manager, Mrs. Nancy Cadena (not pictured)